Pops 3

Wise Publications
London/New York/Paris/Sydney/
Copenhagen/Madrid

Exclusive Distributors:
Music Sales Limited
8/9 Frith Street, London W1V 5TZ, England.
Music Sales Pty Limited
120 Rothschild Avenue, Rosebery, NSW 2018, Australia.

Order No. AM952589
ISBN 0-7119-7239-7
This book © Copyright 1998 by Wise Publications

Compiled by Peter Evans
Music arranged by Stephen Duro
Music processed by Allegro Reproductions
Cover photograph of Mariah Carey courtesy London Features International

Printed in the United Kingdom by
Halstan & Co Limited, Amersham, Buckinghamshire.

Your Guarantee of Quality

As publishers, we strive to produce every book to the highest commercial standards.

The music has been freshly engraved and the book has been carefully designed to minimise
awkward page turns and to make playing from it a real pleasure.

Particular care has been given to specifying acid-free, neutral-sized paper made from pulps
which have not been elemental chlorine bleached. This pulp is from farmed sustainable forests
and was produced with special regard for the environment.

Throughout, the printing and binding have been planned to ensure a sturdy, attractive publication
which should give years of enjoyment.

If your copy fails to meet our high standards, please inform us and we will gladly replace it.

Music Sales' complete catalogue describes thousands of titles and is available in full colour sections
by subject, direct from Music Sales Limited. Please state your areas of interest
and send a cheque/postal order for £1.50 for postage to:
Music Sales Limited, Newmarket Road, Bury St. Edmunds, Suffolk IP33 3YB.

Visit the Internet Music Shop at
http://www.musicsales.co.uk

Barbie Girl *Aqua* 4

Can You Feel The Love Tonight? *Elton John* 26

Don't You Love Me *Eternal* 8

Honey *Mariah Carey* 12

How Deep Is Your Love *Take That* 16

I Believe I Can Fly *R. Kelly* 22

I'll Be Missing You *Puff Daddy* 18

Killing Me Softly With His Song *The Fugees* 29

Say You'll Be There *Spice Girls* 32

Think Twice *Celine Dion* 36

Time To Say Goodbye *Sarah Brightman & Andrea Bocelli* 39

Torn *Natalie Imbruglia* 42

You Must Love Me *Madonna* 46

Barbie Girl

Words & Music by Soren Rasted, Claus Norreen, Rene Dif, Lene Nystrom, Johnny Pederson & Karsten Delgado

To Coda ⊕

5

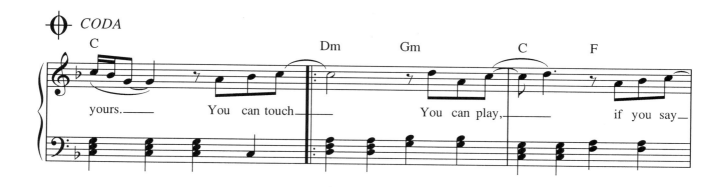

Don't You Love Me

**Words & Music by Cynthia Biggs, Carolyn Mitchell,
Terence Dudley & Christopher Kellum**

Moderately

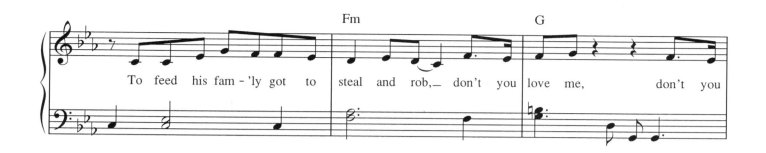

To feed his fam-'ly got to steal and rob,_ don't you love me, don't you

love me no more?_ All I want to know is do you love_ me,_ do you

love me, don't you love me no more?_ All I want to know is do you

love_ me,_ do you love me, don't you love me no more?_

1. Cm

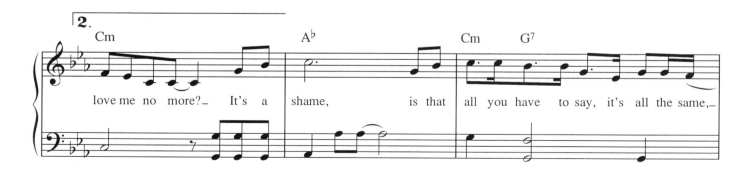

2. Cm

love me no more?_ It's a shame, is that all you have to say, it's all the same,_

if you just turn and walk a - way,_____ when some - bo - dy

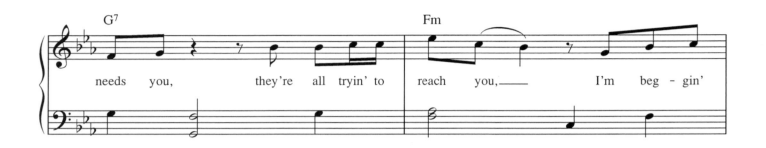

needs you, they're all tryin' to reach you,_____ I'm beg - gin'

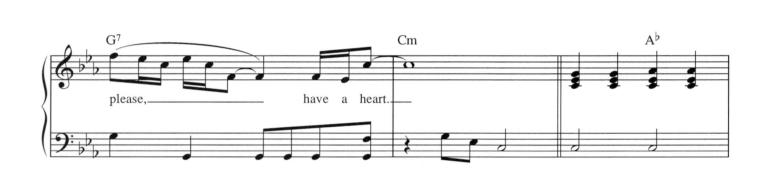

please,_____ have a heart._____

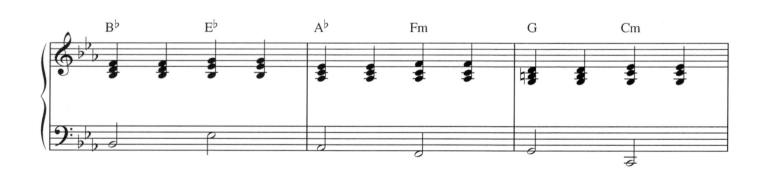

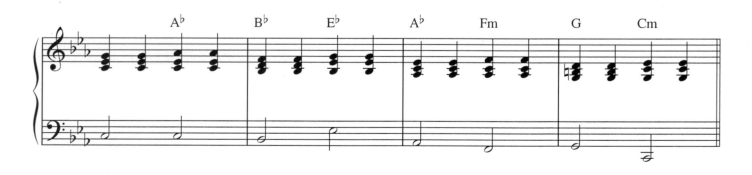

All I want to know is do you love me,— do you love me, don't you

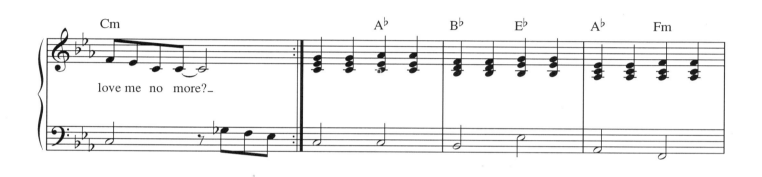

love me no more?_

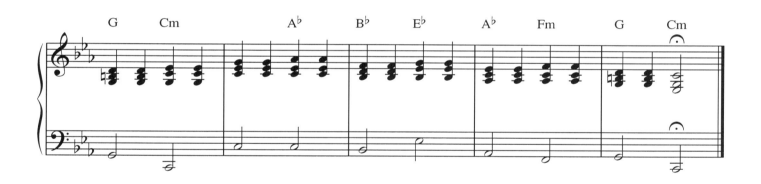

Verse 2:

Vicki's Granny has to walk the streets,
Don't you love me, don't you love me no more?
Tryin' to find herself a place to sleep,
Don't you love me, don't you love me no more?
See the cops arrest another kid,
Don't you love me, don't you love me no more?
Mother's crying don't you know where he is,
Don't you love me, don't you love me no more?

Honey

Words & Music by Mariah Carey, Sean "Puffy" Combs, Kamaal Fareed, Larry Price, Steven Jordan, Bobby Robinson, Stephen Hague, Ronald Larkins & Malcolm McLaren.

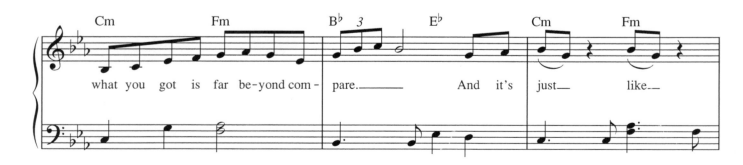

ho - ney____ when your love comes ov - er me____

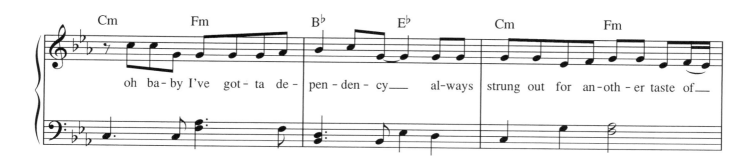

oh ba - by I've got - ta de - pen - den - cy____ al - ways strung out for an - oth - er taste of____

your ho - ney____ s'like ho - ney when it wash - es ov - er me you know

su - gar ne - ver ev - er was so sweet and I'm dy - in' for you, cry - in' for you

I a - dore you.____ One hit of your love ad - dict - ed me, now I'm

strung out on you dar - ling don't you see ev-'ry night and day I can hard - ly wait for an -

- oth-er taste of ho - ney. Ho - ney, oh I can't des - cribe— how good it
(2nd time Rap)

feels in-side.— Ho - ney, oh I can't des-cribe— how good it feels in -side.—

Oh oh oh oh ev - 'ry lit - tle thing you do.

Oh oh oh oh ho-ney got me hooked on you S'like

ho-ney when it wash-es ov - er me you know su-gar ne-ver ev - er was so sweet and I'm

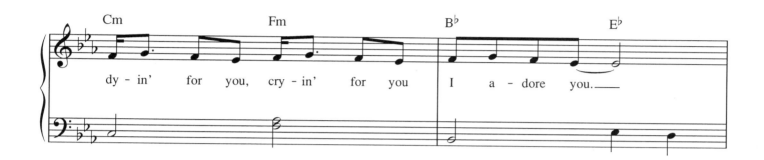

dy - in' for you, cry - in' for you I a - dore you.___

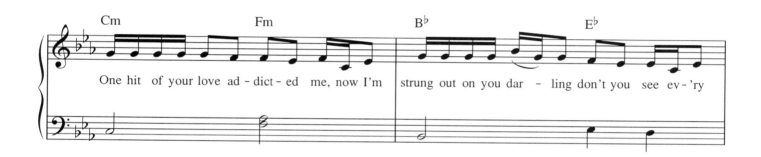

One hit of your love ad - dict - ed me, now I'm strung out on you dar - ling don't you see ev - 'ry

D.S. and fade

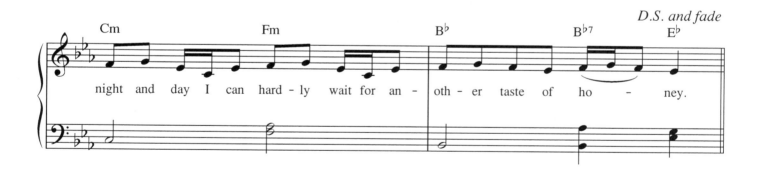

night and day I can hard - ly wait for an - oth - er taste of ho - ney.

Verse 2:

I can't be elusive with you honey
Because it's blatant that I'm feeling you
It's too hard for me to leave abruptly
'Cos you're the only thing I wanna do.

And it's just like honey *etc.*

Rap:

How in the world we won't stop
And Mariah you're on fire
How in the world we won't stop
So Mariah take desire
Break down.

How Deep Is Your Love

Words & Music by Barry Gibb, Robin Gibb & Maurice Gibb

17

I'll Be Missing You

Words & Music by Sting, T. Gaither & F. Evans

Moderately

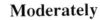

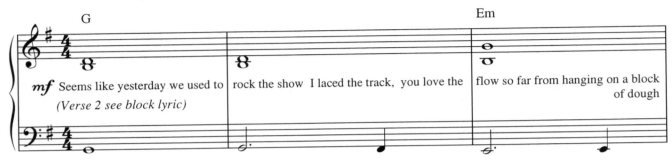

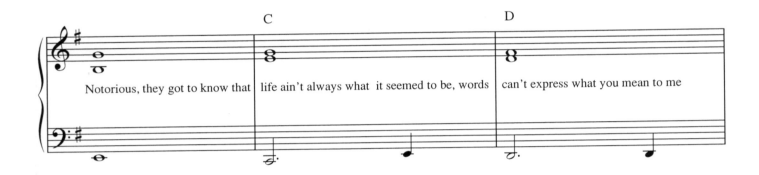

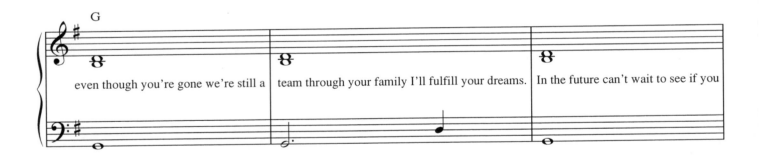

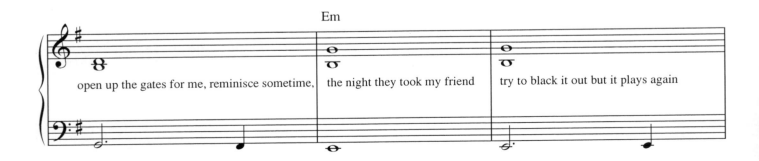

what a life to take what I'm bound to break I'll be miss - ing

you.

From that morn - ing when this life is

ov - er, I know I'll see your

face. Ev - 'ry night I pray

Verse 2:

It's kinda hard with you not around
Know you're in heaven smiling down
Watching us while we pray for you
Every day we pray for you
Till the day we meet again
In my heart is where I keep a friend
Memories give me strength I need to proceed
Strength I need to believe.

Heart so big I just can't define
Wish I could turn back the hands of time
Us in a six, sharp and new clothes and kicks
You and me takin' flicks
Make a hit, stages they receive you on
Still can't believe you're gone
Give anything to hear half your breath
I know you're still living your life after death.

I Believe I Can Fly

Words & Music by Robert Kelly

Moderately

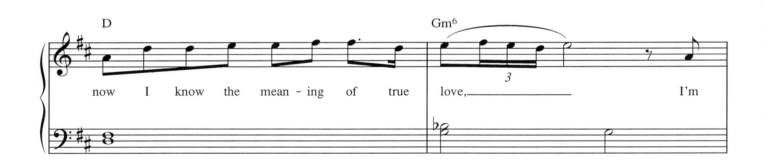

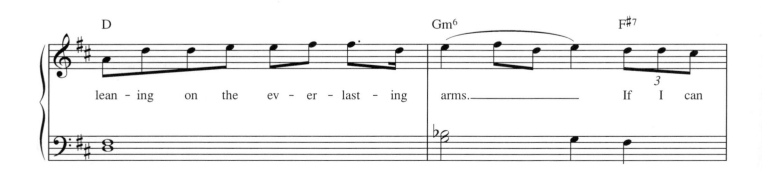

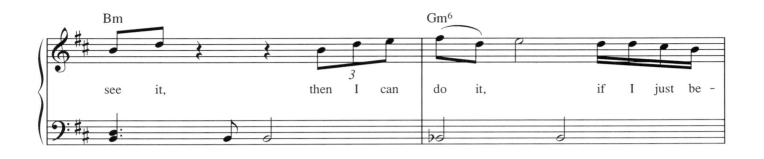

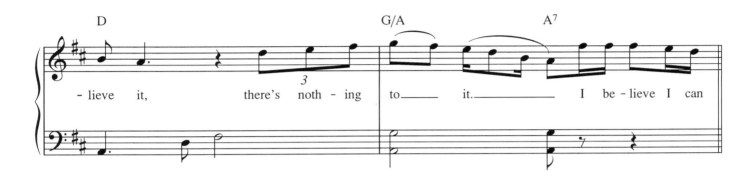

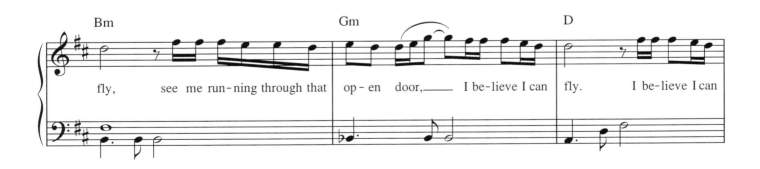

night and day,___ spread my wings and fly a - way,___ I be - lieve I can

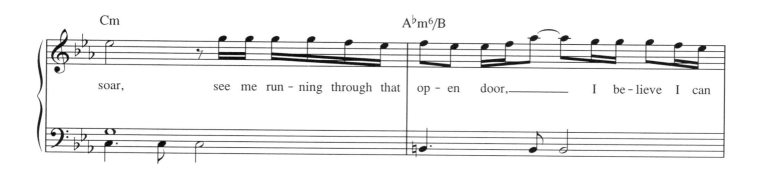

soar, see me run - ning through that op - en door,_____ I be - lieve I can

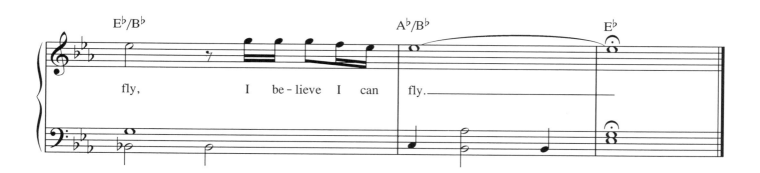

fly, I be - lieve I can fly._____ I be - lieve I can

Verse 2:

See I was on the verge of breaking down,
Sometimes silence can seem so loud.
There are miracles in life I must achieve,
But first I know it stops inside of me.

Oh, if I can see it,
Then I can be it.
If I just believe it,
There's nothing to it.

I believe I can fly *etc*.

Can You Feel The Love Tonight?

(from Walt Disney Pictures' "The Lion King")

(as performed by Elton John)

Music by Elton John. Words by Tim Rice.

Moderately

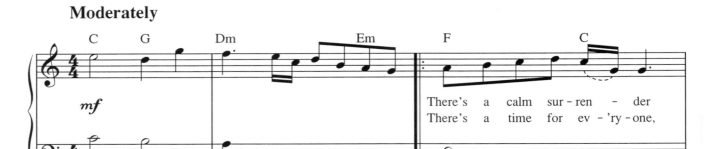

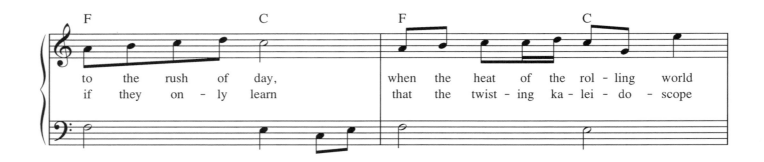

-lieve the ve - ry best

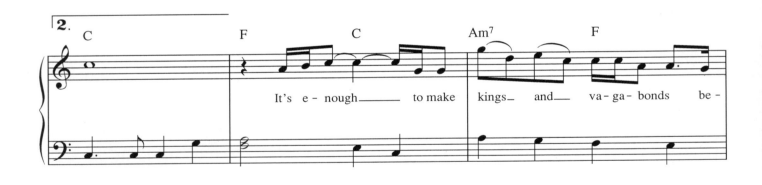

It's e - nough_____ to make kings__ and__ va - ga - bonds be -

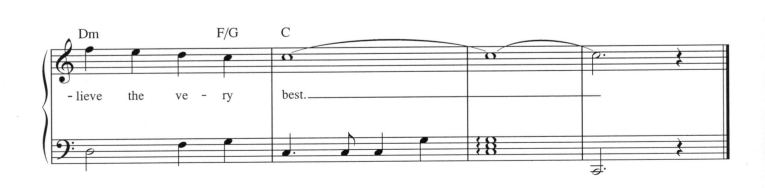

- lieve the ve - ry best._____

Killing Me Softly With His Song

Words by Norman Gimbel. Music by Charles Fox.

Slowly

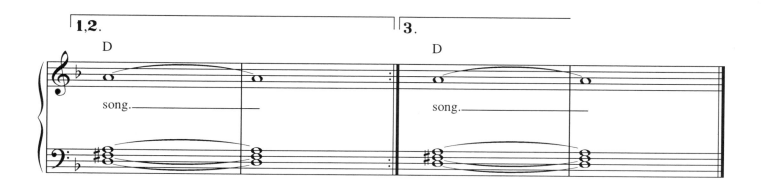

Say You'll Be There

Words & Music by Eliot Kennedy, Victoria Aadams, Melanie Brown, Emma Bunton, Melanie Chisholm & Geri Halliwell

Moderately

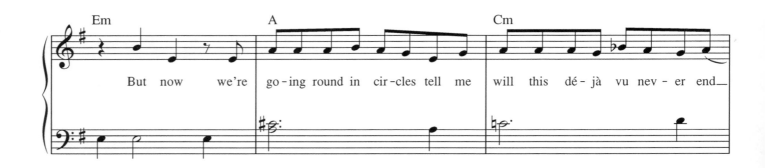

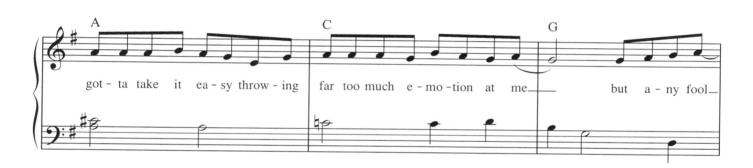

34

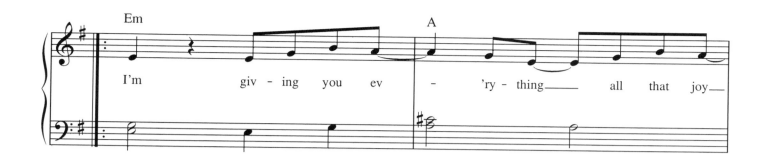

Verse 2:

If you put two and two together you will see what our friendship is for,
If you can't work this equation then I guess I'll have to show you the door.
There is no need to say you love me it would be better left unsaid.

I'm giving you everything all that joy can bring this I swear,
And all that I want from you is a promise you will be there,
Yeah I want you.

Verse 3: (Instrumental)

Any fool can see they're falling, gotta make you understand.

Think Twice

Words & Music by Andy Hill & Pete Sinfield

you— or us?——— Ba - by,—— don't say what you're a - bout to say,—

— look back be - fore you leave my life. Be sure be - fore you close that

Repeat to fade

door, be - fore you roll————— those— dice. Don't

Verse 2:

Baby think twice, for the sake of our love,
For the memory,
For the fire and the faith
That was you and me.
Babe I know it ain't easy
When your soul cries out for higher ground,
'Cause when you're halfway up
You're always halfway down.

But baby this is serious,
Are you thinking 'bout you or us?

Time To Say Goodbye

Words & Music by F. Sartori & L. Quarantotto
Adapted by Frank Peterson

Moderately

Quan-do sei lon-ta-na sog-no l'o-riz-zon-te man-can le pa - ro - le.

si lo so che non c'é lu-ce u-na stan-za quan-do man-ca so - le, se non ci sei

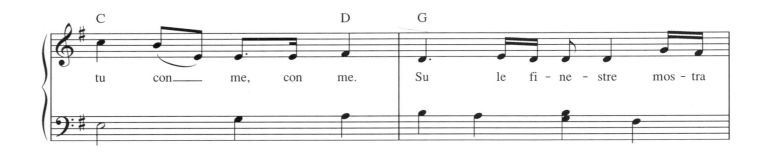

tu con___ me, con me. Su le fi – ne – stre mos – tra

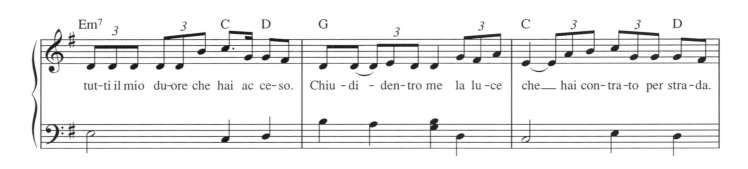

tut-ti il mio du-ore che hai ac ce-so. Chiu – di – den-tro me la lu -ce che___ hai con-tra-to per stra-da.

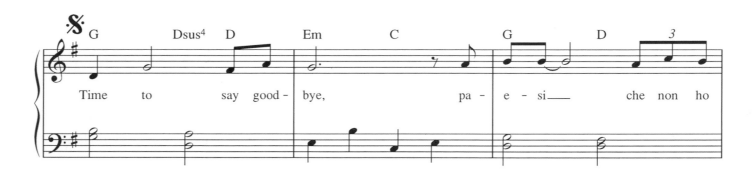

Time to say good- bye, pa – e – si___ che non ho

mai, ve – du – to vis - su to con me, a – des – so si, li vi –

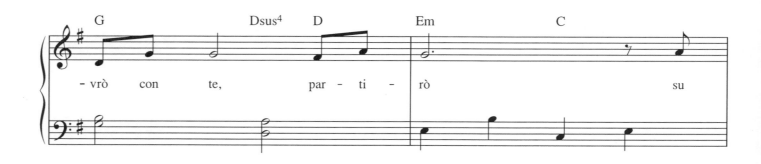

– vrò con te, par – ti – rò su

na - vi per ma - ri   che io lo   so,   no, no,non e - si - sto - no   più,   it's time to say good-bye.

Quan - do sei lon - ta - na sog - no l'o - riz - zon - te man - can le pa - ro - le.

E io si, lo so che sei con me, con me,   tu mia lu - na, tu sei qui con me,

mi - o so - le tu sei qui con me,   con me,   con   me,   con me.

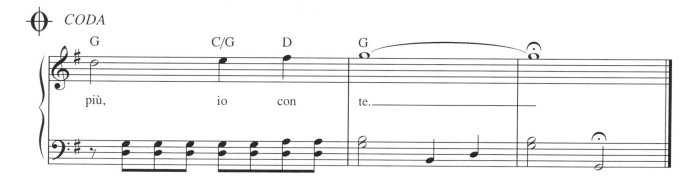

più,   io con   te.___

41

Torn

Words & Music by Anne Preven, Scott Cutler & Phil Thornalley

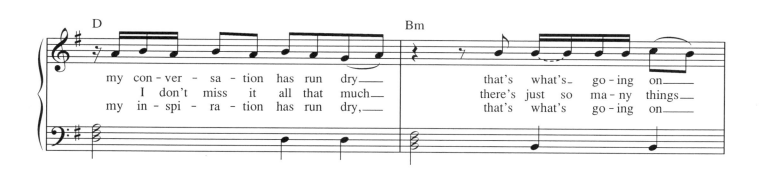

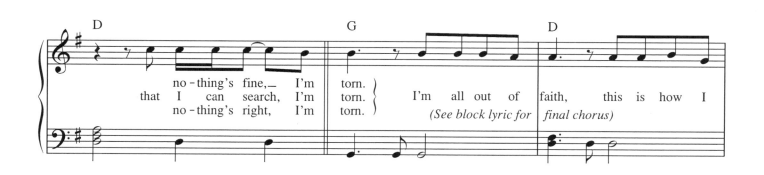

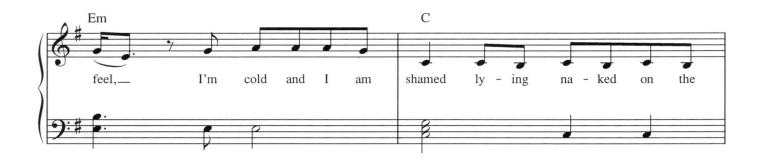

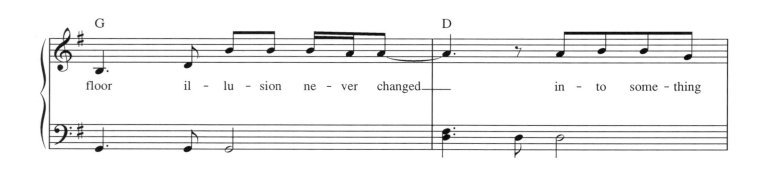

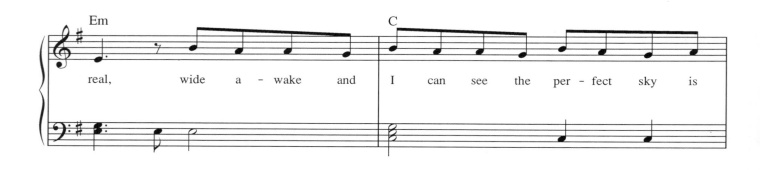

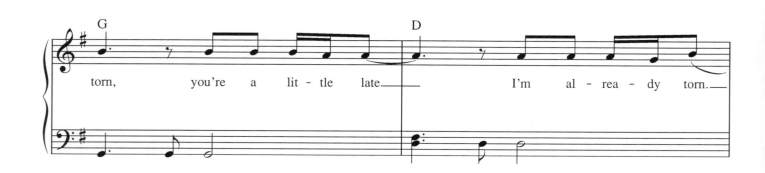

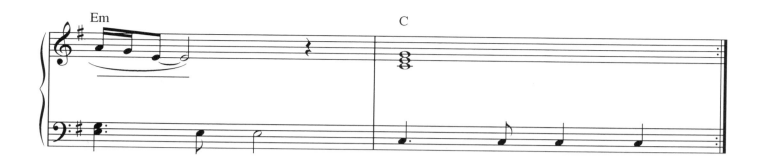

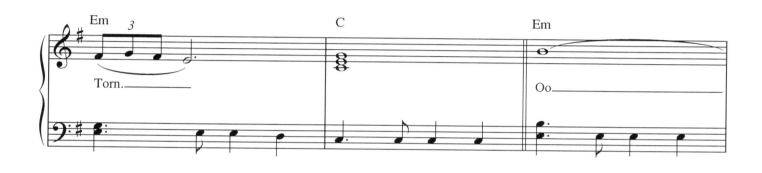

Torn._____

Oo._____

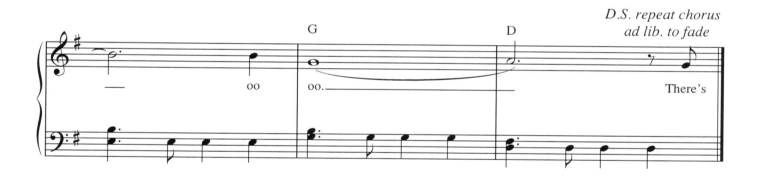

_____   oo   oo._____   _____

There's

*D.S. repeat chorus
ad lib. to fade*

Final Chorus:

I'm all out of faith
This is how I feel
I'm cold and I'm ashamed
Bound and broken on the floor.
You're a little late
I'm already torn
Torn.

You Must Love Me

Music by Andrew Lloyd-Webber
Lyrics by Tim Rice

Moderately

1.Where do we go from here? This is-n't where we in-
mf (Verse 2 see block lyric)

-tend-ed to be.___ We had it all,___ you be-lieved___ in me,___ I be-

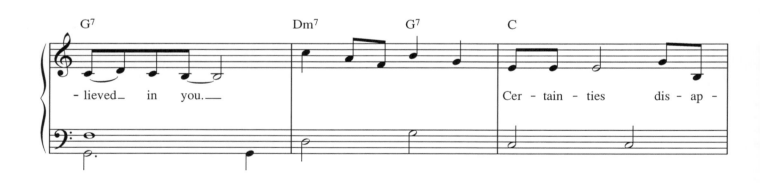

-lieved___ in you.___ Cer-tain-ties dis-ap-

-pear what do we do___ for our dreams to sur-vive,

how do we keep____ all our pas - sions a - live as

we used to do?____ Deep in my heart I'm con -

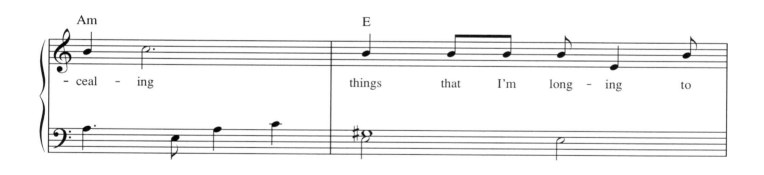

- ceal - ing things that I'm long - ing to

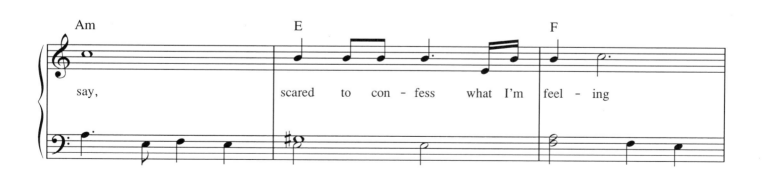

say, scared to con - fess what I'm feel - ing

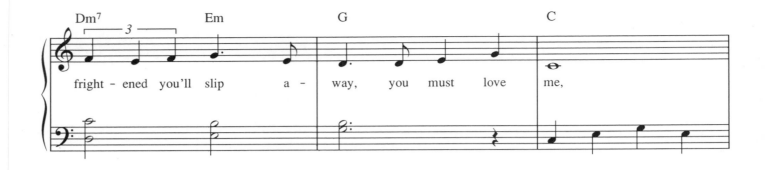

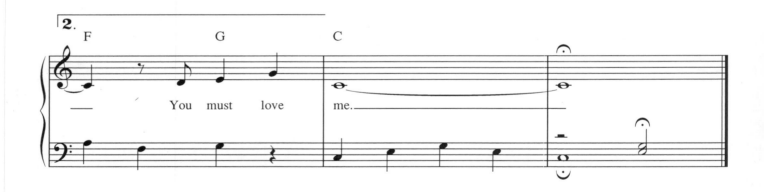

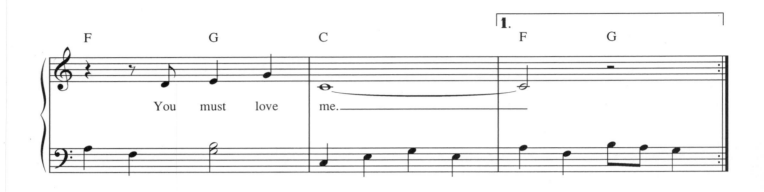

Verse 2: (Instrumental 8 bars)

Why are you at my side?
How can I be any use to you now?
Give me a chance and I'll let you see how
Nothing has changed.
Deep in my heart I'm concealing
Things that I'm longing to say,
Scared to confess what I'm feeling
Frightened you'll slip away,
You must love me.

8/99 (35066)